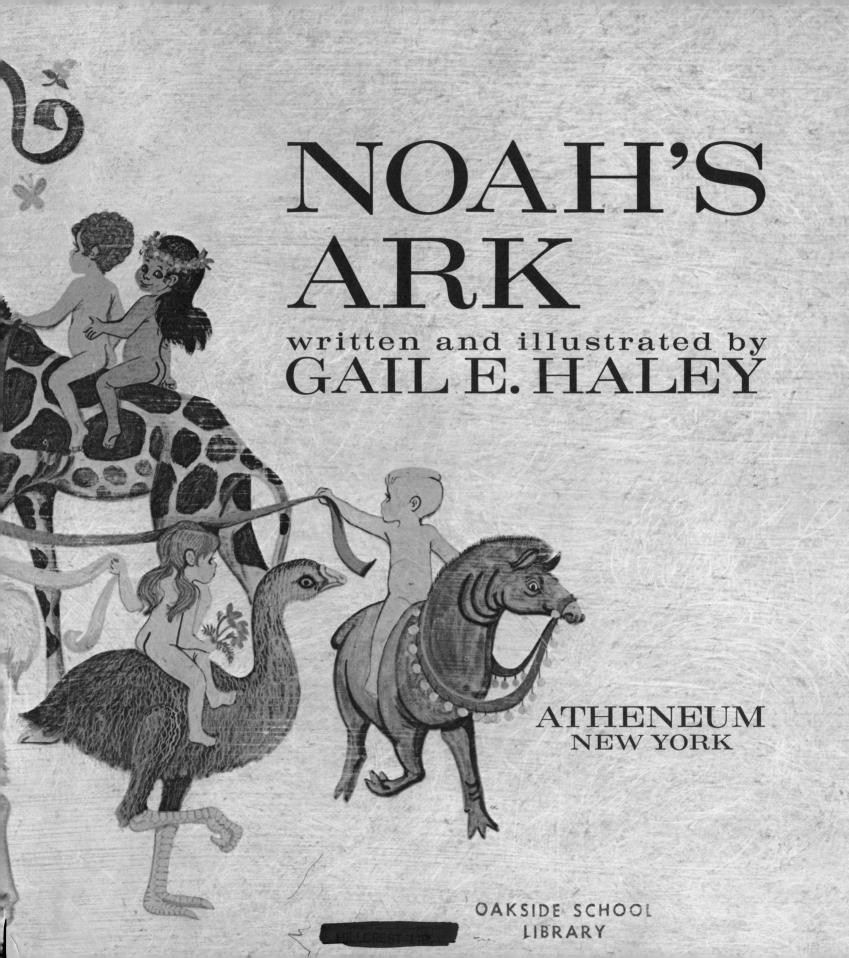

NOAH'S ARK

written and illustrated by
GAIL E. HALEY

ATHENEUM
NEW YORK

This book is dedicated to
Francis, Marguerite and Geoffrey—the crew;
to Arnold, the Captain whose sure hand guides our course;
and to the Ark, which will preserve those things we hold dear.
With special thanks to Jean Karl.

E
H

5131

...Every beast of the earth
...every fowl of the air
...all that moveth upon the earth
...all the fishes of the sea...
   into your hands are they delivered.
                              —Genesis 9:2

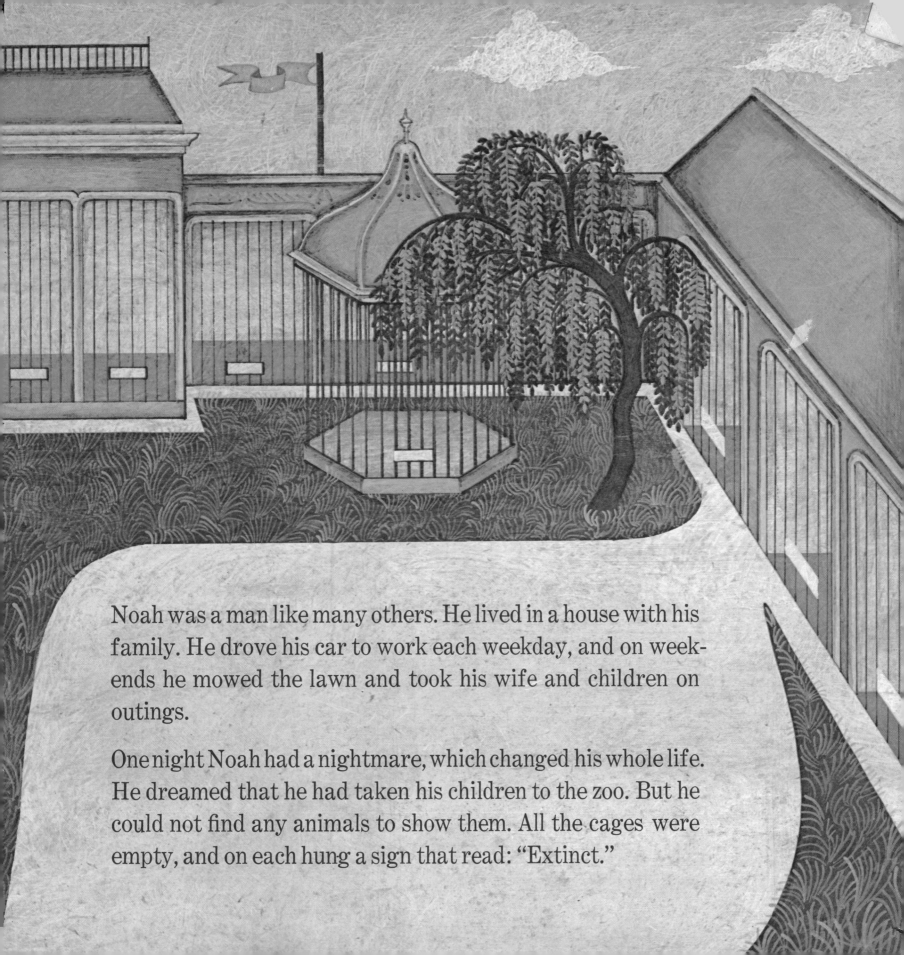

Noah was a man like many others. He lived in a house with his family. He drove his car to work each weekday, and on weekends he mowed the lawn and took his wife and children on outings.

One night Noah had a nightmare, which changed his whole life. He dreamed that he had taken his children to the zoo. But he could not find any animals to show them. All the cages were empty, and on each hung a sign that read: "Extinct."

Noah's nightmare was so terrible that it woke him up. Although it was still dark, he put on his clothes and went for a walk through the town, hoping to forget his dream. But what he saw in the lighted shops only made him feel worse.

He saw coats made of the skins of wild animals in one window. In another there were hats covered with the feathers of rare birds. He even found a store that sold only animal trophies.

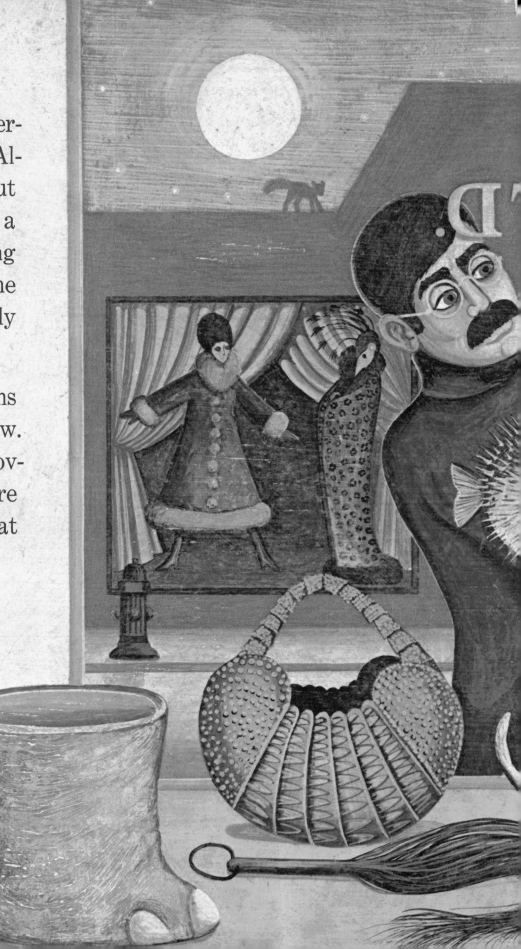

Sadly, Noah walked on until he came to a high hill over-looking the city. The sun was just rising, but it could not brighten what he saw. The city was dirty; there were no parks or forests; the air was filled with smoke from factory chimneys; the river was brown, sluggish and lifeless.

"My dream could come true," thought Noah. "The animals will become extinct if there is no place for them to live."

Noah tried to warn others that the animals were in danger. He wrote letters and he made speeches, but no one seemed to share his concern. Finally, he appeared on TV and pleaded with the people of the world: "Please help me save the animals."

Nothing changed, despite all of Noah's efforts. Only then did he realize that it was up to him to save the animals.

Noah sold everything he owned; he bought an old wooden barge and rebuilt it. He added a solarium and filled it with trees, grass and flowers. He built a fresh water pool, stalls, perches and cupboards. He even put in a deep freeze so that arctic animals would be comfortable.

Noah turned the ark into a floating home for every kind of animal.

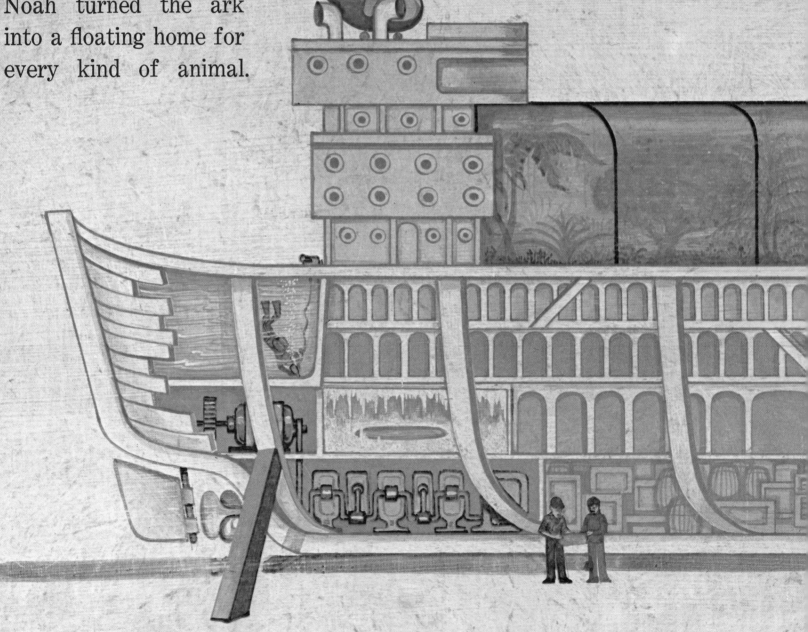

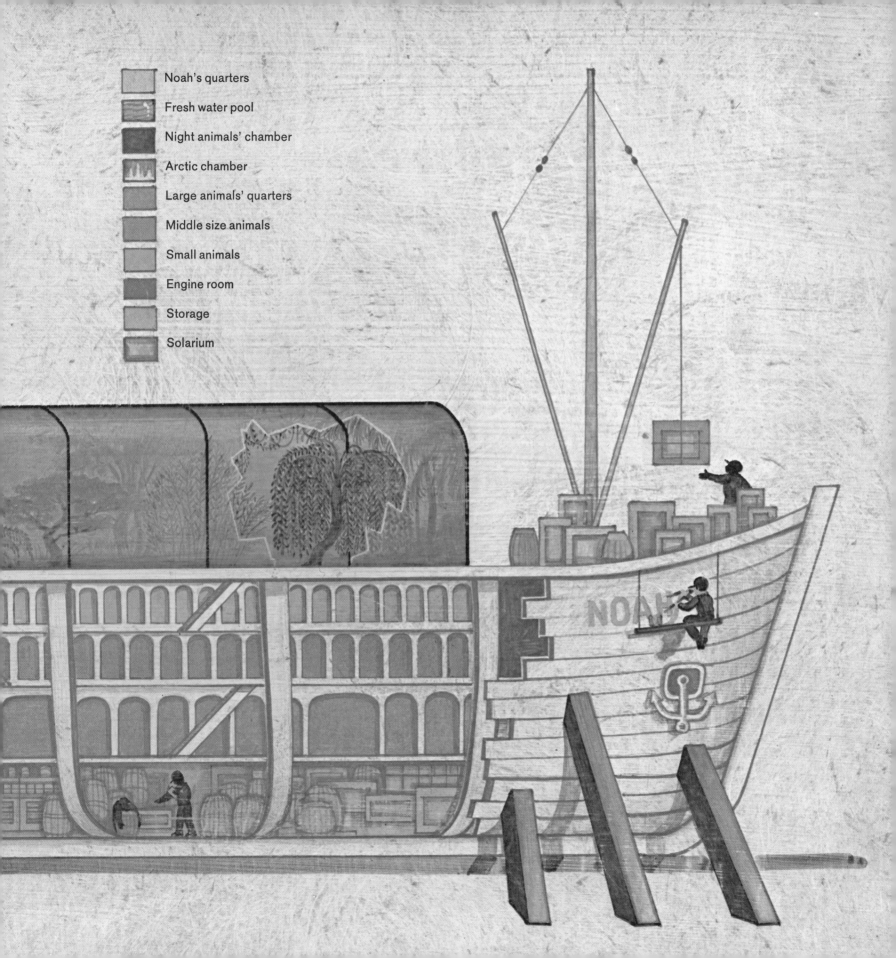

Noah's quarters

Fresh water pool

Night animals' chamber

Arctic chamber

Large animals' quarters

Middle size animals

Small animals

Engine room

Storage

Solarium

Noah stocked the ark with foods and medicines for a long voyage. He moved aboard with his wife, with his children and some of their friends. They then set sail to every continent to find and save whatever animals were left.

Noah invited one male and one female of each kind of animal to join him. They boarded the ark two by two. Only the ostrich refused to leave his home. He hid his head in the sand and would not listen to Noah.

When all the animals were safely settled, Noah turned the ship toward the open sea, where the sun still shone and the air was fresh.

At first, the rocking of the ark made the animals sick. They lay about sadly, wishing they were back on land. But soon they became accustomed to the motion of the boat and began to eat and play.

As time passed, the animals grew bored and restless and started to misbehave. Cats chased mice; the hippopotamus shoved the rhinoceros; the polar bear went fishing in the pool; and the lion and the tiger had a terrible fight. The ship was bedlam until the animals heard Noah's big voice:

"Stop this fighting at once," he scolded. "You are acting like people."

Ashamed, the animals made up and the ark sailed on in peace.

All the animals aboard the ark had babies. Animal and human children grew up together and invented games the world had never seen before.

Life was so pleasant and gentle that they almost forgot about the land.

One day, many years later, the ship's radio crackled: "Calling Noah's ark."

Noah sat down at the controls and put on his ear phones. The animals crowded around the door. "Noah's ark here. Come in."

"Do you really have animals aboard your ship?" asked a voice.

"Yes," said Noah. "Two of each are here, together with many animal children."

"Then they are the only ones left in the world," said the radio voice. "Will you please bring them back?"

"We will never return until the rivers and the air are clean and men have made the land beautiful once more."

The ark sailed on.

Much time passed before another message came over Noah's radio. Now the caller promised that the land was ready to receive the animals. Noah's son, by now a grown man, took the ship's helicopter to see whether it was true.

The rivers, streams and lakes sparkled; the sky was clear and blue; men lived in tall houses surrounded by forests, gardens and parks. Noah's son took the happy news back to the ark. And Noah knew that it was time to return to land.

ORDER OF DEBARKATION

The ark docked in a peaceful harbor. The animals and their children streamed ashore.

They were not put into cages, but were petted, fed and allowed to roam about at will. There was no longer any need for zoos.

WELCOME NOAH'S ARK

Men and animals lived together hap-
pily forever after. But the ostrich was
never again seen on earth.